CONSTANTIA SOTERIOU was born in Nicosia in 1975. Her novels *Aishe Goes on Vacation* and *Voices Made of Soil* were shortlisted for the Greek and Cypriot National Book Awards. Her short story 'Death Customs' was the winner of the 2019 Commonwealth Short Story Prize. Her short stories have been translated into English, Italian, Danish, Turkish, Serbian, and Ukrainian, and appeared on BBC Radio 4 to celebrate the tenth anniversary of the Commonwealth Short Story Prize.

LINA PROTOPAPA is a translator and literary critic based in Nicosia. Her translation of Constantia Soteriou's 'Death Customs' from the Greek received the 2019 Commonwealth Short Story Prize, while her translation of Nikolas Kyriacou's 'The Debt' was shortlisted for the same prize in 2020. Her work has appeared in *Granta*, *adda*, *Fractal*, and *Hartis Magazine*, and on BBC Radio 4.

BRANDY SOUR

CONSTANTIA SOTERIOU

Brandy Sour

Translation by Lina Protopapa

**FOUNDRY
EDITIONS**

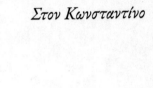

Στον Κωνσταντίνο

CONTENTS

Trauma always has a homeland:
a village, a house, a battlefield, a camp, a country

LIBBY TATA ARCEL

BRANDY SOUR: THE KING

They say that a barman invented the cocktail for King Farouk of Egypt in the 40s – a dark time for the king, who is already grown and in trouble, no longer the handsome, athletic boy charming Europe with his Western manners but a heavy, middle-aged man facing all kinds of political headaches in Egypt – and elsewhere, too – who has to conceal his fondness for alcohol. They say that he had come to Cyprus for a break after a trip to England; that he stayed in Platres, the island's most cosmopolitan village; and that he lodged in the only hotel that could possibly host him, the Forest Park. They say that he stayed in the village for a single night – just time enough to compose himself. They say that he had booked an entire floor of the hotel and had shut himself away in a room for hours and hours, eating and drinking – as he always did – and smoking too. They say that what keeps you awake at night in Platres are the nightingales, but what keeps Farouk awake are the problems back in his country; his break-up with Farida, who gives him nothing but daughters;

the English and the French, who keep running their greedy hands all over Egypt; his belly, which keeps growing bigger and bigger. They say he was spotted opening the window that night and breathing in the sweet smells of the village – the lavender and the perfume of the ancient pine trees that cover the long Troodos mountain range and reach all the way down to the village – and the chill of the night that carries the world's secrets. They say that he'd had a rough day, that he'd previously met with the island's English governor and that they'd got into an argument. The crisis that will pull him from the throne is only a few years away. The death of him. Farouk is tired. They say that, his head heavy from all the food and politics, he left his attendants in the room and went to the bar incognito. They say that he sat at the hotel bar alone and asked the barman to fix him something. "Fix me something," said Farouk to the barman. "Fix me something to drink that doesn't look like a drink, fix me something that doesn't look like it contains alcohol, fix me something that isn't what it seems, put in a bit of that good brandy of yours that I like so much. Oh and add some lemon too – I like your lemons." It's true what he said about our lemons, we have good lemons. The man behind the bar listened sympathetically to Farouk and poured all his mastery into a drink worthy of kings who want to deceive people: he added brandy to help the king forget and lemonade to sweeten him, but also sour lemons to remind the king of his sorrows and Angostura bitters to make him bitter, and he poured it all into a highball glass so the drink would resemble an iced tea. "Here you go!" Before you fill the glass with all the ingredients, you must first sugar its rim. And, lastly, you must top it all off with a sweet little cherry. A maraschino cherry. King Farouk tastes the drink the barman makes for him and he sighs. He likes its sweetness and its sourness, and he likes how it leaves a bitter aftertaste on his tongue that reminds him of Egypt. He sits at the bar and talks for hours to the man who had fixed his drink. The crisis that will pull him from the throne is only a few years away. The death of him. But everything seems distant this evening, with the drink that sweetens him and leaves a bitter aftertaste in his mouth. When he leaves the island the following morning, he takes with him fourteen okkas of halloumi, twenty-one okkas of sour cherry jam, three okkas of lavender tea, two okkas of that damask rose lotion that soothes his skin after the harsh sun, seven bottles of Commandaria, and the complaints of the employees to whom he left not one mil in tips. Despite pressure from Farouk, the barman refuses to give the king the recipe of the drink he created for him, and Farouk leaves, his luggage packed with everything but this secret recipe for the cocktail, the one made especially for him, the one made for people who want to deceive. The barman will take the secret recipe and the secrets of the king to his new job, to the new Big Hotel that will shortly sprout in the island's capital. This is the new drink he will serve in the cool verandas, in nice highball glasses, full of secrets and brandy and lemonade. Cyprus has good lemons. It's a good drink, brandy sour. They say that King Farouk liked it a lot.

It's a Cypriot drink that the barman will subsequently make famous, that he will serve to actresses and cosmonauts and kings and guerrillas in the Big Hotel that will later appear. It's a Cypriot drink, with ingredients from our island, that you serve in a tall glass after you sugar its rim, a drink full of cognac and lemonade that seems and tastes innocent but is not. It's a drink worthy of kings who want to deceive people, a drink that isn't what it seems to be, that looks like iced tea and that you can drink publicly without anyone knowing what it contains. It's a drink full of secrets – that's why it was made here. Cognac, lemons, and Angostura to make you bitter – it's not a brandy sour if it doesn't make you bitter.

BRANDY SOUR

In a highball glass:
1 part cognac
2–3 drops Angostura bitters
Lemonade
Sour lemons
Soda water
1 glazed cherry on a toothpick
We rim the glass with sugar
We decorate with a slice of lemon and the cherry, and we offer it to the king.

LAVENDER TEA: THE JEW

The nightingales wake him at the break of dawn. Whatever the weather, he always leaves the window slightly open so that he can hear them. The singing of the birds and the cool air remind him of Zurich and Germany. Then he drinks the hot lavender tea that the young maid leaves on the bedside table and goes for a walk up in the mountains. He knows the villagers find him odd. In a village full of labourers and farmers, people find it strange that somebody would so eagerly seek physical exercise and the weariness that comes with it. Nevertheless, they greet him on their way to work: "Good morning, Mr Architect. Enjoy your walk, Mr Benzion." They are open-hearted people, simple and friendly, and they insist on treating him to figs and other delicacies. He declines all the gifts except the lavender bunches, which he hands over to the maid so she can prepare his hot lavender tea in the morning. It's wonderful, this tea – so typical of the village, so aromatic and luscious. He didn't know lavender was a thing you could drink, a thing you could eat. His mother only used it to perfume her clothes and her linen. Mother, lavender, Zurich, Germany, the cold. "Good morning, Mr Benzion. Enjoy your walk, Mr Architect." His mother, her lavender, his Zurich, their Germany, the cold. He thinks about all this all the time as he walks in the morning, or rather he walks all the time so he might forget all of this. No one in the village knows how he ended up on the island – who brought him here, how long after the war he arrived – nor do they know why he is so highly sought after, so much so that no house, no building, no hotel is constructed without him. He seems to be involved in everything, and everyone wants his advice: let's ask Mr Benzion, they say, let's see what he thinks. Nor does anyone know much about him: who he really is, where his loved ones are, if he likes being here all the time, and if he enjoys what he does. All they know is that he demands good pay – "he is a Jew, after all," they say, repeating the trope they have heard, as though he weren't the first Jew they had ever met; that he dislikes the heat and drinking – he loathes alcohol – and that he always speaks slowly and softly, with his hands in the pockets of his black jacket; that he only ever wears black; and that his English is inflected with a heavy German accent. And he doesn't say much either, he's a man of few words: "He talks like a man who knows fear or who has once known fear," the village priest once said about him. A man who loves walls more than he loves other people, that kind of man. A man who loves walls only, stones only, buildings only. His mother, her lavender, his Zurich, their Germany, the cold. That kind of man. Everyone on the island – the English governors and the local bourgeoisie too – respects him. Perhaps they are even a little intimidated by him. He doesn't feel at ease with anyone, but what he does feel is a slight affinity with the simple villagers who offer him their lavender. After all, he is not on the island to make friends; he is here to build houses, he is a man who loves walls. His first project was a cinema theatre in Limassol, a building with sharp lines – austere, like him. That's the building Skyrianides, a rich merchant from the village, sees; that's why he asks him to oversee the construction of his new hotel, the Forest Park. Others will follow. Everyone who's anyone in the city wants a house designed by "the Jew". As long as they can afford it. And as long as they can convince him. As a matter of fact, they say he isn't too adamant about keeping to his sharp Zurich lines, that he is willing to accommodate the owners' wishes, that he is willing to build them the houses they want. If one knew him better, one would think he likes to make people happy. But nobody knows him. For a few years, he goes back and forth between Jaffa, Limassol, and Platres. His cold. Jaffa is too warm for his taste – too warm to bear, really. And there is a lot he can no longer bear. Platres. His cold. Sometimes he even thinks he could stay here forever, in the village with the nightingales that wake him at the break of dawn. He could stay here forever if he wanted to. "You could stay here forever, if you wanted," the maid tells him in the morning as she leaves his bed to prepare lavender tea for the two of them. It's wonderful, this tea – so characteristic of the village, so aromatic and luscious. He didn't know that lavender was a thing you could drink, a thing you could eat. He didn't know he could be thinking of staying here forever. His cold. It's never cold in Nicosia. The city is a boiling pit in the summer. It's a lot like Jaffa, only with a dried-up river, the Pedieos, and with space enough for a new hotel. "This is something only you could do, something only you could design," Skyrianides tells him. He offers him iced lavender tea flavoured with honey in a tall glass full of ice. He didn't know that you could also drink this tea iced, he didn't know that only he could build this new gem of a hotel, the most exquisite hotel in the Middle East and the Mediterranean too. Skyrianides gives him full permission to build the walls of his dreams, as long as there's something of the island about them, something of its stones, something of its colours and its tradition. "Something of the island's heat," he tells him. His cold. He could stay here forever, in the village. He didn't know that lavender was a thing you could drink, a thing you could eat – he didn't know. Instead, at daybreak, he leaves for Bellapais Abbey; he strolls around the monastery's courtyard for days on end, studying the building. If you were to look at the new hotel he designs on the banks of the river, you would easily make out the lines and the architectural principles of the monastery in the yellow sandstone so typical of the buildings all over the island, in the pointed arches, in the antefixes. The hotel comprises three floors; ninety-three rooms, each with its own bathroom and telephone; a dining room; a ballroom;

and 1,350 electric bulbs that light it up. Seen from a distance, the pointed arches in the portico, at the entrance, and on the facade, together with the tall windows, resemble lavender flowers.

LAVENDER TEA

A small bunch of dried lavender flowers
Very hot water
You let the flowers steep in the hot water for two minutes
You strain
You flavour with honey, if you wish
Helps you forget.

COMMANDARIA: THE MAID

Of all the foreigners she encountered in the hotel, the one she will always remember is Yuri Gagarin. Not Princess Margaret, not Aliki Vougiouklaki – with whom everyone was in love – not even Elizabeth Taylor. She will only remember Yuri Gagarin because he once left the earth and soared to the heavens and saw the earth from afar and the moon from up close. Of course, when she goes up to the village to visit her family, those few days when she takes her leave, the people there are more interested in hearing about the hotel and its great luxuries. Nobody can fathom that each room has its very own bathroom with its very own tap with hot and cold water where the foreigners can bathe whenever they want – even every day, if they wish – and a ballroom and a hairdresser and a tennis court. "What's a tennis?" Everyone wants to hear about the Venetian room, the large ballroom with the oak floors and the Italian chandeliers and the marble imported from Greece. And about the balls, the beautiful gowns the women wear, the elaborate hairdos, the drinks and the food. She answers their questions tirelessly: she tells them about the big rooms with the bright lights and the marble floors and the tall windows that, seen from a distance, look like lavender. Ever since she left the village, she wants nothing to do with lavender. She doesn't want to look at that tea, let alone drink it. She answers the villagers' questions with remarkable patience. Everyone in the village wants to know about the big hotel, about what it's like to live that way. Sometimes somebody asks if she's ever seen a princess; more rarely, they ask if she's seen Vougiouklaki. So far, nobody in the village has asked her about Gagarin. Nobody wants to know about Yuri. Nobody in the village cares that he has travelled from the earth all the way to the stars, that he's seen the moon from up close. Perhaps it's because in the village the stars seem close at night, and the moon looks close too, and they can see it all. But she remembers Yuri. She always remembers Yuri. The sensation he caused when he came to stay at the big hotel for a few days; how everyone wanted to see him from up close. Perhaps it's because, over here, it's harder to see the stars from up close. Perhaps they care more about the moon in the city. That's why they take him from city to city and show him off. The city people flood streets and neighbourhoods, they literally hang from balconies because they want to see Gagarin from up close. "Yuri Gagarin / went up to the moon / brought the Americans / a mushroom to chew." In the cities, that is. Yuri Gagarin. Who chose a small room to stay in at the hotel, with a slanted window that doesn't look

23

up to the sky but looks out to the garden with the damask roses. Of all the guests she encountered in the hotel, she will always remember Yuri: his pale face, his small hands, his slim fingers, how minute and fragile he looked and how much he liked to sit alone in a corner at night, sipping the ancient wine. Commandaria. Gagarin did not drink cocktails. He insisted on ordering sweet Commandaria. In a tall glass with lots of ice, enough ice to water it down. Gagarin's Commandaria was nothing like the Holy Communion the priest offered them back in the village, the sacramental wine in the small spoon, the take-eat-drink-ye-all – no, Gagarin's Commandaria reminded her nothing of god, and the only thing she regrets is not having asked, not having found a way to ask him if, when he had travelled all the way up to the stars and saw the moon, he had managed to see god too.

COMMANDARIA

Highball glass
Lots of ice
For cosmonauts and all those who want to see god.

SHERBET: THE YOUNG LADY

You scoop out the sherbet with a teaspoon and you put it in a tall glass full of water and you wait for it to bubble up. Then the glass fills with foam and the bubbles tickle your nose. If you put it in a tall, narrow-stemmed glass and you climb up the stool and stand in front of the mirror next to your mum, you can imagine you are at the ball. It helps if your mum is already getting ready to go dancing with Dad or to go and listen to George Dalaras or somebody called Messiè Moustakì. You don't like it when Mum and Dad go out and you stay home with Grandma. Mum, who knows this, lets you watch while she gets ready because you like it. You choose her dresses together and her shoes too, and you laugh heaps when she makes her hair big. You like watching her apply grey eyeshadow on her eyelids and lipstick on her lips, and when you look at her in the mirror like that you think your mummy really is the most beautiful mummy in the world. She looks like a princess, and that's why Daddy takes her to a palace when they go out. You know this because sometimes, in the afternoon, Mummy takes you to the Palace too. You've been there at birthday parties, at Maria's masquerade ball, and at Aunty Pepi's wedding reception. That's where Mummy and her girlfriends take their tea and that's where Mr Polys makes cakes: the best chocolate cake in the world, and also a cake with white sponge that Mummy likes because she says it contains kitro-milaki liqueur. Only in a palace can such chocolate cakes be made with syrup and so much chocolate. That's what makes the palace a Palace. You want to have your birthday party at the Palace too and you want Mr Polys to bake your birthday cake. And you won't offer juices and soft drinks but sherbet so that you and your girlfriends can make-believe you're drinking champagne. When you grow up, you too will get married in this palace and you will drink real champagne, not sherbet like Mummy wants you to drink. And you will take your tea there with your girlfriends and you will go there with your husband to listen to Dalaras and Messiè Moustakì. When Mummy comes to give you a kiss, you hug her tight and you think that she really does look like a princess. She is stunning in her beautiful dress and her big hair. That's why she goes dancing in that palace. When you grow up, you will go to that palace too. You will be a princess too and you will drink champagne and eat chocolate cake with lots of chocolate.

SHERBET

Cold water
In a champagne flute
For princess mummies
And young ladies who can't wait to grow up.

VSOP BRANDY:
THE GUERRILLA FIGHTER

The people in the lounges of the big hotel love their brandy: they pour it into deep glasses that look like tulips and serve it slightly cold, just cold enough that, by the time it's in the hands of the gentleman who will consume it, it's at room temperature and may then adapt to his own body temperature. The ladies never take their brandy straight; when they have some, it's in a cocktail in a long-stemmed glass. The local ladies and the English ladies too have a predilection for cocktails containing brandy served in long-stemmed glasses. The guerrillas in the mountains drink it straight out of the bottle. The ladies and the gentlemen, be they locals or English, prefer VSOP brandy. Up in the mountains, when they send Demetris to shop for supplies, he goes for KEO. It leaves a bitter almond aftertaste that he likes. We never use KEO for brandy sours; we only use VSOP. Demetris has never had a brandy sour, but he hears that the people at the hotel love it. He confirms this soon enough when he starts working at the bar there, serving drinks and brandy to the English and the others – the locals. He wears dark trousers with a crease, a perfectly ironed white shirt, and well-polished shoes. The maître d', who's in charge of the staff, is very strict and won't even allow him to use brilliantine in his hair: "This is a serious hotel. Forget everything you ever knew." The English seem to feel very much at home in the serious hotel, laughing a lot and letting go, unbuttoning their shirts a little, joking about the heat and about the locals, not the ones who rub shoulders with them at the hotel, the other ones, the ones who live in the villages. It's the first time Demetris has worked as a waiter and he likes it. He hears the beautifully spoken Greek in the lobby and also some Turkish and lots of English too; he serves drinks to the English and gathers information that he then passes on to his captain. It's a serious hotel. The English seem to feel at home: they laugh a lot and they let go and they joke about the heat and other things, too – things they shouldn't joke about – and Demetris passes everything on to the guerrillas up in the mountains. The English here are nothing like the English he sees on the streets: they wear their uniforms loosely and they laugh out loud and they offer Demetris cigarettes and conspiratorial pats on the back and they sometimes bring him magazines with shameless naked women who seem to laugh out loud too. They also prefer KEO brandy and they ostentatiously shun brandy sours. Demetris looks at them and laughs; he has recently become friends with a Johnny and a Bryan.

One evening, after his shift, the three of them sit out in the garden with the jasmine, and Bryan shows Demetris some photos of his girlfriend, Jane, and his dog, Ruth, back home, and they drink brandy straight out of the bottle. One day, shortly before the annual ball of the Caledonian Society, where all the island's high society will gather – ladies and gentlemen, locals and English – Demetris installs a make-shift bomb in the ballroom. Four people are injured, a maid and three Englishmen, none of them seriously. He is, in any case, arrested and locked up in the English jail with four others. And this is a pity because he will never be able to work in the hotel again and as a consequence he will miss the exhibition of Adamantios Diamantis's paintings, which is the talk of the town in 1957; the exhibitions of the naïf painter Michalis Kashalos in 1962 and 1963; as well as the luncheon served in the ballroom by the last governor of the island, where Makarios and Fazıl Küçük will also be present. Celery consommé, lobster Parisienne, fondant potatoes, seasonal vegetables, salade grecque and peach Melba will be on the menu. And wine, with which the Archbishop will only wet his lips. He, Demetris, found out that they did not offer any brandy in the end. They did not offer brandy at the end of the meal.

VSOP BRANDY

Brandy glass
Room temperature
Can also be drunk straight out of the bottle.

JASMINE TEA: THE POET

He will first try jasmine tea at a Chinese restaurant in his beloved England. They will serve it to him in a teapot after the dessert, pouring it into minute porcelain cups with no handles – it will be a little bitter. The people on the island don't drink jasmine; they pick its tiny flowers at night and string them tightly through a threaded needle and they make necklaces and little bracelets with them. Nicosia has the most beautiful jasmine. It doesn't matter whether you drink its flowers or wear them around your neck, jasmine takes care of you all the same: it makes you feel better, it has soothing properties, and it boosts your confidence. It boosts your confidence when you sit out in the jasmine garden of the big hotel to take your morning cup of coffee and the minuscule flowers fall from the trees and fill up your cup. It boosts you at night, too, when you stand at the window smoking, your eyes piercing the night in search of the "Gothic buildings, the walls, the courtyard of the Great Inn. The narrow alleyways with the rare passengers." This isn't the East. Here is more of a Mediterranean hue. After all, they don't drink their jasmine around here, they string it into necklaces and little bracelets. They wear it around their necks and their hands, and when its blossoms wilt they put them in their linen and pillows. Here, where the miracle happens still, the jasmine blossoms at night in the beautiful hotel gardens, its smell so sweet it's almost sickly. Here, where you can go searching for a homeland you never even knew existed. You, a foreigner, a diplomat, searching in the little city corners and in the sunset and in the jasmine for that which you couldn't find in London and in the East. On the island, poems offer themselves to you – time and the muse ordain that you visit. It's only a few years before you are called to play a role in the future of this island. They use jasmine differently in your beloved England, but here is another place and here is another way. This here, yes, may indeed be the lost corner of Hellenism – except at night when the muezzin calls you to prayer, when the Armenian ayran seller calls you to buy the good ayran, when the Turkish cleaning lady hangs the jasmine necklace around your neck.

JASMINE TEA

In tiny cups with no handles
Also stringed through a threaded needle for necklaces and
bracelets
Gives you a boost and fills you with confidence.
For lost homelands and diplomats and diplomat poets.

ZIVANIA: THE ARCHBISHOP

Zivania is a favourite of the villagers up in the mountains. They pour it into tiny shot glasses and they down it all in one go at weddings and big celebrations. They drink it when they close deals. In the cities, when people celebrate, they drink wine. When they close important deals, they pour some wine on the ground, for the soil to drink. The English drink whisky in big celebrations. They don't like zivania – no need for their throats to burn that way. The Archbishop does not drink zivania – he despises all alcoholic beverages and he doesn't eat any meat either and he only drinks water. Behind his back, the priests accuse him of being a little conceited. Zivania he uses only for having his back rubbed. There's an old man in the archdiocese who's good at cupping and bruising it. He sources his zivania from some of his people back in the village; they make it themselves. He doesn't remember much about the village – he left for the monastery when he was little – but he does remember the big black cauldrons where they distilled zivania and he remembers his father, too, telling him that they looked the same as hell's cauldrons. Zivania is no good for drinking. He only ever uses it for his back rubs. Whenever he has a big decision to make, he calls the villager to cup his back until it's bruised black, until it hurts. Zivania stings him and it comforts him too, helps him clear his thoughts, lends him his majestic posture when he walks with his shepherd's crook with near-regal grace. It lends him that bold, noble air when he stalks into humble village churches and into the lavish lounges of the Big Hotel. They don't serve zivania at the Big Hotel – they consider it a lowly drink; during big celebrations and weddings and the closing of deals they serve cognac and whisky and wine. Brandy sours, too, with Cypriot brandy and Cypriot lemons. When he goes to the hotel, the Archbishop asks for cold water. The maître d', who knows him well, adds ice cubes and a slice of lemon. He serves it in a highball glass. The Archbishop wraps his fingers around the glass ever so gently, his eyes, half closed, examining the large chandelier in the Venetian hall, the luxurious furniture, and the decorated ceilings. He much prefers the lounge bar's hardwood floor. He may not be a drinker but he is very much a smoker – an avid one at that. He likes smoky rooms and the words of journalists who speak from behind their glasses. The words that inadvertently escape with the alcohol. This is why he doesn't want to drink. When he is faced with the biggest, hardest decisions, alongside the cupping he also takes to walking: he walks along the Troodos Mountains, beneath the tall trees; he climbs up the mountaintops like he used to when he led the sheep to graze, before he left for the monastery; he walks downhill until he reaches the small villages, until he can smell the lavender in people's gardens. He is, and always has been, a shepherd. Shepherds walk a lot and they don't drink alcohol. They only drink water. When he isn't walking up the tall mountains, he walks along the long river that starts at the place that will become his presidential palace and ends near the Big Hotel. He carries his water flask with him when he walks. The tall mountain is known for its cold, crystal-clear water. In the small villages they distil pure zivania for the harsh winter days. For drinking, but also to remove stubborn stains when all else fails, and to preserve things inside, things they want to keep forever. The Archbishop has gallons and gallons of zivania stored in the archdiocese – there's no need for the old man to bring his own zivania when he cups his back with the tiny cups, the Archbishop contemplates. He contemplates, too, the Struggle, the English, the guerrillas, Greece, Enosis. The harder things become for the Struggle, the more the zivania stings his back and the longer he walks up in the Troodos Mountains. He doesn't drink at all, he doesn't eat meat either – he eats very little in general, but he smokes incessantly. When the end of the Struggle is in sight, he will walk kilometre after kilometre underneath the ancient trees of Troodos. During the luncheon that the governor hosts on the occasion of the Declaration of Independence, he wets his lips willy-nilly with a bit of wine and sits up in his chair straight and rigid. On the night he announces his ultimate compromise vis-à-vis the future governance of the island, the villager cups his back until it turns black; litres and litres of the drink evaporate from his body. When the time comes, he leads the efforts to rename the street in front of the big hotel, the one dedicated to King Edward. He is also the person behind the acquisition of the imposing mansion next to the hotel that will later house the offices of the Greek embassy. Since he hasn't succeeded in making the country Greek, let him by all means make the hotel Greek. When he visits the United States, he may agree with Kennedy about bringing the Hiltons to Nicosia, and he may indeed recognise the need for more hotels to be constructed and for the country to invest in tourism, but the Big Hotel, the one at the heart of the island, is another story. When the Egyptian investors sell their shares in the hotel, he personally intervenes in order to deter Forte, the British company, from buying them out: he worries that behind the company lurk Turkish interests. In a single night, the hotel passes into the hands of the archdiocese, into Greek hands, and the Archbishop shakes hands and pours wine onto the ground, and the Turks now no longer pose a threat to the hotel. It belongs to the Church when the terrible battle with the Turks takes place there in 1974; it belongs to the Church when the negotiations over the Cyprus problem commence between Clerides and Denktash, pragmatic and cosmopolitan men who have a taste for good food and good drinks; it belongs to the Church when it ceases to function as a normal hotel.

Clerides looks to the future – he doesn't hesitate to ask for some zivania during the negotiations held in the Venetian room. Despite what you might think, the winter in Nicosia can be bitterly cold, and zivania can help warm you up and sometimes clear your mind. The Archbishop is categorically opposed, though; he continues to drink only water and to smoke and smoke and smoke. When the coup happens, three massive tanks will roll up in front of the Big Hotel. When, three years after the coup, the Archbishop suffers three consecutive heart attacks in the space of six hours and dies, everyone will say that his heart stopped beating due to the pain, and the autopsy will show that his heart is cracked, that it presents signs of hypertrophy, that it weighs almost five hundred grams, and it will be sent off to London for further examination. In the end, it will be embalmed and preserved in alcohol, in pure zivania, and kept at the archdiocese as an exhibit for years until it is finally buried together with his body high up on the island's tallest mountain. Where the clearest crystal water runs.

ZIVANIA

In a small glass
Ice-cold
You can also use it for back rubs or to store a big, betrayed
heart.

AYRAN: THE TURK

Every day, he takes the shortcut from King Edward VII Street and walks past the big Greek hotel on his way to work and it's right there, on a nearby street, that he buys his ayran every day from Mr Alexian. Not everyone knows how to make a good ayran; you need the right kind of milk – goat's milk – to make yogurt with, and then you need to add milk – goat's milk – to the yogurt and whisk it all well to make a good ayran. Then you need to add salt and lots of spearmint. Mr Alexian knows his ayran: he's Armenian. In Turkey, where he'd been before, they made their ayran with lots of salt but no mint, but as his grandmother used to say, you can't have ayran without the mint. Best not to have ayran at all if it has no mint. Sometimes, he thinks that the reason he likes this drink so much is that it reminds him of his grandmother, so much so that he can put up with the bewildered stares he gets from his compatriots and from the hotel valet, too, as he walks by. One day, supposedly by chance, somebody from the Greek side comes up to him and asks: "Where is it you go every morning, and why do you always have to walk past here?" A few days after the question, the street in front of the big hotel, which was once named after the British king, is renamed Markou Drakou after the new national hero, and then one morning, he sees people installing sandbags there, and with his poor Greek he gathers that this is a measure taken to protect hotel guests from potential Turkish Cypriot fire. For an entire month, he can't go through at all, and he can't buy his ayran until the UN remove the sandbags from the area. And he misses that drink, he misses it as dearly as he misses his grandmother. The last time he attempts to walk past the big hotel, they stop him and tell him he needs to go back. He needs to find another way to work, another way to get his ayran; or maybe he needs to stop drinking it altogether – or find another place to buy it from. In a matter of days, everything will change. He won't be able to pass through: the city will be divided into sections, his people confined in enclaves. Nobody understands his need to drink ayran, the drink his grandmother taught him to drink. He'll manage to sneak to Mr Alexian's one more time for one last ayran. It's from him he will find out that it's not a good idea to walk past the Big Hotel any more. Mr Alexian tells him that the whole situation frightens him very much, that he is very worried about what's to come, and then he bids him farewell and treats him to his last ayran. He adds salt and lots of mint too. Best not to drink ayran at all if it doesn't have lots of mint. In a few days, everything will change: he will need to find a new way to work, or perhaps he will need to change jobs altogether, and maybe he'll need to stop drinking the drink his grandmother loved so much. In the end, he will get a job as an assistant in his uncle's law firm in the old city centre, close to the Saray Hotel. It's their hotel, the Turkish one, grand and luxurious like the hotel the others built, where the headquarters of the Ottoman governor of the island once sat. That's what "Saray" means in Ottoman, after all: palace. The Turkish hotel is taller and bigger, and it offers a view of the old city and the Big Hotel. Each have their own, his uncle tells him while they have their coffee – it's coffee, now – in the morning. Each in their own home, on their own side, at their own hotel. Isn't it better to drink coffee in the morning instead of that atrocious ayran?

AYRAN

Yogurt
Cold goat's milk
Whisk both well
Add spearmint and a bit of salt
Best not to drink the ayran at all if it has no mint.

PISS: THE PAINTER

He first finds ancient stuff when he is ploughing. Although he is a cobbler by trade he also ploughs his handful of little plots of land to make ends meet. Life is hard, his village treeless: Ashia, they call the village. Shadeless, the village with no shade and with no trees and also without much oil. The people here go hungry. He goes to bed wanting to make more money and he wakes up wanting to make more money. "Money, that's all you dream about," his wife tells him, and it's true; he wants money, he wants more money, and he goes to sleep and wakes up thinking about how he's gonna get the money to raise his children and live his life and be well. "Always after cash, you," the villagers tease him. Cash money. Cash in your hands. Kashalos. That's what the villagers call him. He's always after cash. Money. The first time he finds ancient stuff is when he is ploughing. He accidentally shoves his ploughshare a little deeper into the ground and he brings jugs and ancient things up to the surface. Whole, intact jugs – well made, too – with decorations: jugs like the ones his mother used for storing wine and oil, like the ones his wife still has at home. On Sunday, at the coffee shop, he tells the others about the ancient stuff, about the decorated jugs. "Sell them to Mr Suthery," the villagers instruct him. He, Mr Suthery, collects ancient stuff and pays in pounds sterling. Money. Kashalos hears about the Englishman, he hears about the money, and on Monday he wears his best vraka, puts on his nice little hat, and picks up the ancient stuff and goes to the capital to meet him. The Englishman takes a look at the ancient stuff, takes a look at the jugs, takes a good long look at Kashalos, opens his pouch, and pays him handsomely, in golden coins. Money. "If you have more of these, bring them to me." Kashalos returns to the village bedazzled – three golden coins for the jugs that are buried in dirt, useless jugs that the ancients used for their food, for storing their oil – and he feels pity for the Englishman buying this useless stuff, and he starts ploughing his plot deeper and deeper; the jugs down there can feed his children better than wheat ever could, better than the shoes he makes ever could, and he ploughs his land every day, he digs the ploughshare deeper and deeper, he finds some coins. This time, the Englishman doesn't pay well. He wants a head from him, he says, if he can find one: "A. Head," he tells him. "You. Find. Head." Kashalos goes back to his plot, he pushes his ploughshare deeper, he looks for heads: nowhere to be seen, these ancient heads – someone must have beaten him to it. He goes to the village priest to ask for a newspaper, to ask if he can tell him, if he can show him what these heads look like. The heads Englishmen want. Money. At night, he takes to sculpting. He sculpts an Apollo and an Aphrodite – those are the names the ancient heads had in the priest's newspaper, the heads of his ancient people. All night long he keeps at it: he sculpts and sculpts and then at the break of dawn he buries the heads in the ground and he leaves them there in the muddy soil and every day he pisses on them. If you piss on the heads that you sculpt, they turn yellow and they look ancient, and you can sell them for more – you take them to the Englishman and the Englishman thinks they are real and he gives you four pounds and he asks that you bring him anything else you can find. Kashalos returns to his village and he starts sculpting heads again and making jugs and forging coins, and he buries everything in the dirt and the mud and he gets up at night to piss on all of it. When you piss on the heads you sculpted and the coins you forged, they turn yellow, more yellow, and they look ancient and you can sell them for more – nothing makes stuff look ancient like piss does – and he keeps making ancient stuff and pissing on it. Then one day the police come to the village to arrest him. "You are a smuggler of antiquities," they tell him, and he protests, he tells the officer that he makes the ancient stuff himself, that it only looks like that because he pisses on it. Then another time the museum director calls for him and shows him some coins and some plates; he is infuriated. "Which ones are yours and which ones are ancient?" he shouts, and then: "You should be ashamed of yourself."

Kashalos looks at the museum director, looks at his plates, and they look ancient – even he has a hard time telling them apart. "Here," he tells the museum director. And then: "What's worse? Selling the real ancient antiquities or selling the ones I make myself?" Money. Kashalos makes money from the antiquities, sometimes a little, sometimes a lot. He keeps grabbing the newspaper out of the priest's hands for inspiration, for ideas on how to make even more money. Then one day he reads in the newspaper about someone who bought some paintings and gave the painter thirty pounds. Now that there, *that's* money. He runs off to the priest to get him to explain, and then he rushes off to the capital and he buys materials and he slowly starts painting, and he paints the world the way he sees it: simply, childishly. He is seventy-odd years old, but he is confident he can paint well. He buys canvases and colours and he starts painting the things he knows: weddings and christenings and harvests and the tools of the land and his world. He paints the things he has come to know. He heaps men and women and customs and joys of every kind in his paintings. He is bold and brave, and one day he goes looking for a great painter called Diamantis – he wants to show him his work. Diamantis goes to his home and he looks at his work, his world, his people, his Cyprus, and he stands still and silent for a moment. "This is what you will charge for your works. We'll set up an exhibition – we'll sell them." At the exhibitions, the works are a hit. They are snapped up. All of Nicosia is raving about the great new naïf painter, and the people in the village coffee shop tease him: "He's done it again, Kashalos – he's found a new way to make cash. You can't say 'Kashalos' without saying 'cash'." In 1962 and 1963, he has solo exhibitions at the Big Hotel: his exhibitions are major social events. The hotel hosts art exhibitions often: of famous and unknown artists, of men and women, of Greeks and Turks, of modern people and ancient people too, of many people of the New World and a few people of the Old World, like Kashalos. During his last show, as he is standing there with his vraka and his headscarf, he suddenly feels like he's about to piss himself and he asks to be shown to the toilet, and he finds himself at a loss before the sumptuous bathroom to which he is led, and he secretly goes outside and relieves himself onto the damask roses in the hotel's back garden. In the years to come, Kashalos paints with a fury and he becomes famous and he goes abroad with his vraka and only in England will he relent and wear trousers, just one time and one time only. He lives in his village now and he tries to convince everyone that they need to remember him as Kashalos the painter and not Kashalos the fraudster who pissed on the jugs and the heads he'd sculpted and sold as ancient stuff to the English. He even makes an offering to the saint and, to atone for all his sins and all the pissing he'd done on the ancient stuff he'd made, builds a church in his village, near his house: Saint Spyridon. But the war breaks out and he never gets to finish his church, and when the Turks come he refuses to leave his village, and when during the first days of the war the heathens leave the old painter alone, he thinks that he can afford to stay there with his wife and to finish his offering to the saint and the frescoes in his village. When one day the Turkish soldiers barge into his home, he reluctantly gives them the money they ask for, and when they think he is lying about not having any more money, they will strike him on his shoulder with a rifle and he will fall down and break his leg. His sons will then spirit him away to Larnaca in a small van. He will die a few days later, in a retirement home, alone and inconsolable, with the name of his village on his lips, his village with no shade, his Ashia. He is no longer a hustler, no longer a painter: he is a refugee. When the big exhibition takes place in the Big Hotel forty-five years later, featuring the works of Greek Cypriot artists that had been returned to the Republic of Cyprus, two of his works will be exhibited, both of which had been found in the Municipal Gallery of Famagusta, one with the tools of the land he had known so well, and one with the women of his land picking cotton, works of an ancient world that, like him, is gone.

PISS

Makes the ancient stuff you make look better, causes fantastic oxidation
For great big painters
with sinful pasts.

ROSEBUD TEA: THE DOORMAN

City people think that flowers are only good for looking at. Village people know that flowers are also good for eating. Especially roses – those tiny pink roses, the hundred-petal roses called damask roses, the ones that climb and spread out their thorns across fences and hedges. You can dry them in the sun and use them to season your food, to make it taste sweet and spicy. His mother has always seasoned her food with roses, ever since she was a little girl: she picks them at night, in August. She picks the tiny little roses – the roses they use to make rose water – and she leaves them to dry out in the sun. Then she puts them inside jars and keeps them out of the heat and humidity. He himself prefers using the roses to make infusions: he picks the flowers on the first night of August and dries them. You have to get the timing right when it comes to roses, you have to pick them with the August dew on their petals – if you pick them too early or too late, you'll get bitter infusions. When he wants to make his tea, he scoops a few petals with a small spoon and puts them in his tin mug, and he lets them steep in cold water overnight until they come alive again. In the morning, he boils them. You can have your rose tea hot or iced, you can have it in the winter and in the summer too, and it's also good for your stomach, it helps digest the indigestible. It's a little sweet and a little spicy – it reminds you of the village and of your mother. Flowers aren't just for looking at. You can eat them too. When he starts working as a doorman at the Big Hotel, he takes his tin mug with him and the root of a damask rose that he secretly plants in the hedge. It doesn't take much for the root to flourish and to grow and to merge with the rest of the rose plants, the English ones that reign supreme in the garden. Although the gardener finds out, he doesn't say anything – he tends to the Cypriot rose too, the hundred-petal rose, the damask rose the doorman carries with him from his village, as he tends to the other roses, the foreign ones, which have wonderful English names such as Queen Elizabeth and Princess Sissi and Landora. The doorman takes his walk around his gardens every day; he enjoys walking around the English gardens, with their many roses that smell wonderfully rosy, the symmetrical gardens with their geometrical patterns and exotic palm trees – certainly very different to his mother's roses back in the village, potted in old tin cans. He loves taking his tea in his tin mug while he strolls in the morning around the garden with all the shapes, next to the garden with the jasmine, before he clocks in, before the hotel guests and the romantic English ladies and gentlemen with their expensive redingotes

49

start flooding the gardens. His stroll in the English garden becomes a necessity. He likes order. And there's something soothing about the garden's symmetry. The garden's roses fill him with joy. Sometimes he gently prunes them with his little pair of scissors and, come August, he then secretly picks the tiny pink roses and dries them for his infusions. When the hotel administration decides to take the garden apart and build a pool, a bar, and a tennis court in its place, he feels like his whole world is coming undone. He barely makes it in time to save a few roses, even though he knows it's the wrong season and they'll make for bitter infusions. As the construction progresses and the English garden gives way to the modern constructions, he feels as though he, too, is wilting. Now he avoids wandering around what once were his gardens – he can't stand to look at the naked women sunbathing where his roses had once been, these modern, urbanite ladies who came to replace the English at the bars and at the receptions. When the English left, they also took the belle époque with them – and his roses. Maybe, he ponders, there is a rose somewhere called Belle Époque. The open bar and the pool attract new visitors to the hotel, which wants to leave its English past behind and become modern and strong, just like the country does. The new bourgeoisie sips cocktails by the artificial water and giggles loudly. The little Turkish kids who manage to slip out from their part of the neighbourhood and poke a hole in the wall by the pool from which to peek, while they piss, at the shameless women and their husbands splashing in the water in their underpants are the only thing that gives him consolation. Instead of notifying the hotel administration, he moves the big potted plant next to the bar, near the hole in the wall, camouflaging it. Now, in the morning, he takes his tea alone in his room, and only at night does he sometimes walk around the outdoor spaces reciting the grief of his roses, naming the places where they had once been. He continues to drink his infusion every day, although it's spicy and bitter now. When you pick the roses at the wrong time, rose tea is no good. You can have rose tea iced or hot, in the summer and the winter too. It's good for your stomach, it helps digest the indigestible, even when it's bitter.

ROSEBUD TEA

In a tin mug
You can drink it iced and hot too
You pick the tiny little buds at night in August and you dry them
If you get the timing wrong, you get a bitter infusion
Helps digest the indigestible.

ORGEAT: THE FILM EXTRA

The first time he ever held a gun in his hands was in 1970, in a film starring Vougiouklaki, when she came to Cyprus to star in a film about the world war, the second one, together with Demetris Papamichael. They were looking for extras for *Lieutenant Natassa*, a film about the Second World War, and they cast him in the role of Soldier B, who will die holding tight on to his gun within the first few minutes of the film. He has to jump from a high hill and someone has to shoot him and he has to die. Vougiouklaki he doesn't interact with much. His scene is with Papamichael, who is a serious, manly man and wants nothing to do with lowly extras. They seem to be very much in love, Vougiouklaki and he, even though they are always arguing; the extra hears their rows and screams all the time, sometimes about the film and sometimes about the acting and sometimes about their son and sometimes about the heat. They are filming in Syrianohori, in Morphou, a place that resembles a desert, a village full of dirt and sand and heat, covered by a heavy, dusty sky. Vougiouklaki is melting in the desert-village. A woman, the wardrobe stylist, is always running behind her with an umbrella, trying to guard her from the sweat and the heat and the bad stuff. Vougiouklaki is really something: she runs; she rolls around in the sand, the heat, the dirt, and she cries and she weeps; but she wants her magnificent hair always to look perfect and she wants herself always to look beautiful. The wardrobe stylist suffers. Papamichael and Vougiouklaki argue. Daytime is unbearably hot and the evenings are bitterly cold in the village. There is a wind blowing from Morphou Bay that pierces you through and through. The crew gather in the village coffee shop, drink wine, and smoke. They discuss the film. Cyprus. The Second World War. They secretly gossip about the protagonist. Who wants to be beautiful in every scene, even when people are being killed. The extra sits apart, looks at the crew, looks at Vougiouklaki, looks at the wardrobe stylist, stands aside – he is, after all, expendable, a Soldier B, and he will die holding on to his gun in the very first minutes of the very first scene of the film. One evening, when the cold breaks your bones, Aliki Vougiouklaki is whining. She is cold, she is hot, her hair is a mess, and she's got into a huge fight with Papamichael. She says that she wants to leave, that she is sick of this village and let's get it over and done with, and she also wants something to sweeten her. And then comes the coffee shop owner offering her the white orgeat in a cracked old mug. Orgeat syrup made from bitter almonds and sugar and diluted with hot water and full of aromas at the coffee shop one evening when the cold pierces your bones.

To sweeten you, to tame your anger. There's a wind blowing from Morphou Bay that freezes you and that can even kill you. Vougiouklaki is delighted: she's never had orgeat before and she is stunned – she asks the coffee shop owner to offer everyone orgeat and she's all smiles and whimsy and she fawns over everyone. The world brightens, the people soften, they start laughing and mellowing – Papamichael too. Even the icy wind outside seems tamer, quieter. The extra is astonished: he understands now why everyone says this woman has a star glowing above her. Or is it the orgeat's fault? Orgeat syrup made from bitter almonds and sugar and diluted with hot water and full of aromas at the coffee shop on a night when the wind goes right through your bones, sweet orgeat that sweetens you, that softens you, that makes the world shine like pearl. When the shoot is over in the village and moves to the Big Hotel, the extra pleads with the person in charge to be hired on the set again – he'll do anything, it's a joy to feel like he's a part of this cause. The Big Hotel turns into a war scene with fake blood, traitorous screams, murder. He is an extra once again, and he dies with pleasure again and again. Soldier A and B and C. An extra. When the film is over, he goes to the cinema with his friends, proud of himself, even though many of his scenes didn't make the final cut. When he walks past the Big Hotel, his memories of the scenes he'd experienced, the miracles, move him. When the war breaks out in 1974 and he is drafted to fight against the Turks, he is one of forty soldiers commanded to keep the hotel under their control until the very end. He takes part in a battle that people refer to as terrible and decisive and fierce, since they are commanded to hold the hotel at any cost. Under no circumstances can the Big Hotel fall into Turkish hands. The exchange of fire is so intense that at times it looks like it's raining bullets. The shells that strike blacken the sky. The Big Hotel turns into a war scene with blood, traitorous screams, murder. He becomes an extra again, and he dies again and again. Soldier A and B and C. An extra. It's July and the heat is unbearable, but he feels a cold inside him, a wind that goes right through his bones, that freezes him, and that can even kill him. And then, unexpectedly, in the midst of all the commotion and the shooting and the screams and the blood, he remembers that fake war, the first time he'd held a rifle in his hands, and he suddenly understands the protagonist's need to be beautiful even when people are being killed. He remembers the orgeat, its sweetness, the beautiful wardrobe stylist, and when a bullet strikes his chest, he falls back with the sweetness of that memory on his lips: the world comes sickly sweet, and then it's gone. Soldier A and B and C. An extra.

ORGEAT

In a cracked old mug
Orgeat syrup made from bitter almond and sugar
Diluted with hot water and full of aromas
When the cold pierces your soul and your bones.

BEER: THE PHOTOGRAPHER

Beer needs to be drunk icy-cold. Especially if it's summer and you're in Nicosia and the sun has done a number on your head because you've been roaming around the city taking photographs all day long. You drink it in a cold glass, or, if you're terribly thirsty, straight out of the bottle. It helps with perspiration, it calms your nerves, it makes you dizzy, and it helps you forget the war for a moment or two. And also the photos of the war you keep taking. The locals on the island first start drinking beer during the time the Big Hotel is being built, just after the Second World War, right around 1950. Before that they drank strong spirits, tea, and wine. Good beer starts being produced on the island in the 50s, when the KEO brewery produces it. KEO is a blond beer conceived by Czech brewers with a long tradition in lager: it has a light taste and a somewhat bitter after-taste – it reminds you of the Cypriot sun and it quenches your thirst and makes you drink in large quantities, but if you aren't careful it can make you dizzy. The English start drinking beer when the British government relocates the infantry cadre from Egypt to Cyprus and the presence of the British army on the island increases significantly, when the English soldiers start frequenting the Big Hotel to blow off some steam. They come here for the beers and the haircuts. They drink beer, they have their hair cut and their moustaches shaved, and they unbosom themselves to the barber. The dusky barber trims their blond heads with his small machine and he freshens up their red English napes with damask rose aftershave. It restores the skin after exposure to the harsh sun. The barber listens to the English secrets and he gathers them like he gathers the blond hairs from the floor. The English go to the Big Hotel for beers and for haircuts. They mingle with the journalists who have travelled there from dozens of places across the world to cover the latest developments in the Middle East and the French and British operations in Suez. They sit at the bar, they drink beers and brandy, and they discuss current events. Tommy has long blond hair and he doesn't need a haircut. He always drinks the blond beer of the island when he comes to the famous bar at the Big Hotel, when he comes back from Czechoslovakia, from Poland, from Chile, from Vietnam, when he takes photographs of the wars other people fight. He likes the bar at the Big Hotel, which has something of the city and something of the village too. He likes the barman, who is olive-skinned and sneaky and smart, and who knows your name and your drink even if he hasn't seen you in months, even if he hasn't seen you in years. He offers everyone else brandy sours; Tommy, though, he immediately gives a KEO beer to when he returns to Cyprus, when he comes back on the island to cover the war between the Greeks and the Turks. The barman likes Tommy, who is blond but lacks the harshness of most English, who only takes photos and doesn't write reportage and doesn't take anyone's side in the war: "Photography is neutral. It instantaneously captures the moment." Tommy is neutral. He clicks the click of war, he takes nobody's side, and he sends the photographs to other people. Sometimes the barman asks him if he misses home, why he likes taking photos, if his job frightens him. Tommy replies that only fools and heroes know no fear. "And which one are you?" Tommy doesn't reply to the barman who offers him the blond beers of Cyprus. Beer is light, but it calms you down; it can make you dizzy and make you forget the war. As the foreign soldiers increase on the island, so does beer consumption. In 1952, beer consumption was a mere 295,000 gallons, then in 1954 it increased by 62 per cent, and in 1962 KEO sales in beer increase to 1,077,000 gallons and in 1968 they reach 1,454,000 gallons, and then in 1974 2,686,714 gallons of beer are consumed on the island, and in July, when beer consumption is at its peak, war breaks out. Tommy remains trapped inside the Big Hotel during the war. He is present during the big battle, the one referred to as terrible and decisive and utterly fierce. He is not at the centre of the action, at the centre of the fighting: he is inside the four walls of the Big

Hotel. He roams around the hotel with his camera hanging around his neck and he hears the bullets whistle around his head. Just like in every other war. Photography is neutral. It instantaneously captures the moment. He clicks the click of war, he takes nobody's side, and he sends his photos to other people. In 1975, his photos, which capture "the agony, the fear, and the tragicness of those moments", receive first prize in the World Press Photo Contest. His photos depict soldiers at the time of battle, foreigners trapped inside the hotel, and the room the photographer stayed in during all this mayhem. His unmade bed with the creased sheets. When the war in Cyprus blows over, Tommy goes to Syria, to Lebanon, to Iraq, to Croatia, to Palestine, and to Kosovo. He continues to take photos of the wars other people fight. He visits Cyprus again one summer, as an old man this time, with short hair. He takes a walk and looks at the Big Hotel from afar. He isn't allowed inside. He buys a cold blond beer and he drinks it all by himself, sitting on a bench. Beer needs to be drunk very cold. Especially if it's summer in Nicosia and the sun has done a number on your head and you remember that barman who remembered your name, who offered you beers and asked whether you were afraid. Only fools and heroes know no fear. "And which one are you?" Beer you need to drink cold – it's light, but it can make you dizzy and can make you forget about the war. And it can make you not have to answer whether you're a hero, whether you're brave or cowardly, or just a fool.

BEER

Blond
You need to drink it icy-cold
You drink it in a cold glass or, if you're terribly thirsty, straight
out of the bottle
Helps with perspiration, calms your nerves, makes you dizzy
Makes you forget about the war for a moment or two.

COFFEE: THE MAÎTRE D'

He always wakes at dawn and he goes to the kitchen to have his coffee prepared just the way he likes it. The only coffee of the day. With lots of kaymak and no sugar. Turkish coffee – Greek coffee, he always corrects himself – with sugar is an absolute waste of coffee. It needs to be bitter. There's no point otherwise. Coffee time is the one moment of the day when he gets to relax. He takes his coffee outside, in the garden with the jasmine, before the hotel guests wake and the day begins. Only once he's had his coffee can the day begin. He manages the staff with an iron fist in a velvet glove and keeps everything under his supervision. The Skyrianides family had him train in Venice. Nothing happens without his approval: from the way the waiters wear their uniforms to the next day's menu. After all, he is the one who has compiled the employee manual with all the relevant protocols and regulations. Whenever there are receptions and balls at the hotel, he is in his element, talking to the people in charge, planning, organising, advising on everything from the menu to the flower arrangements. Everyone knows him and everyone knows that he, the maître d', is the person to call on in case of an emergency. The fashion show organised by "Elegance", the French committee, and the ball of the Medical Society of Nicosia, and the balls of the Caledonian Society, and the art exhibitions, the main topic of conversation among high society, all owe their success to him. He knows every corner of the hotel, every chair, every tiny little piece of it. If it wasn't so trite, one would say the hotel is like his child. Everyone who knows him knows that he, the maître d', is the person to call on in case of an emergency. When the first shots are fired, on the day war breaks out, everyone turns to him. His first concern is to help protect the foreign customers: he is the one who takes the initiative to have them hide in the basement and then escape under UN supervision. As the fighting rages and the bullets mercilessly strike the hotel, he feels as though the weapons are striking his own body. He will never recover from the shellfire. When they receive orders to evacuate the hotel and the hotel eventually ends up in the hands of the UN, he is the one who gives the hotel staff instructions on how to safeguard the furniture and the silverware. When he packs his suitcase and is forced to leave, he feels like he's also taking with him everything that the hotel has ever been. Back at home now, he anxiously follows the negotiations about the Cyprus problem on the TV so he can steal glimpses of the state of the rooms and the verandas. The first thing he realises is that somebody has pulled out the jasmine in a fury. He later finds out that they had died, and that somebody had planted cactuses in their place. In every TV frame, he sees his beloved Venetian room falling apart, the cracked walls, the ramshackle flooring, water leaking everywhere. Meanwhile, the leaders of the Greeks and the Turks continue to meet at the hotel regularly. In his old rooms, where galas and masquerade balls were once held, talks are conducted about the solution to the problem. At some point, he learns that the big ballroom is now the place where Argentine Blue Helmets take their lunch sitting on plastic chairs, and that out in the cactus garden they now drink maté, not coffee. Some afternoons, he arranges to meet with former colleagues in an old coffee shop in town, with the maid and the cleaning lady and the doorman. He's taken to drinking coffee in the afternoon now, too – no sugar, the way it befits funerals and grief and tragedy and death. That kind of coffee. He takes his coffee with thick kaymak and no sugar. Coffee needs to be bitter – there's no point otherwise.

COFFEE (TURKISH, GREEK, CYPRIOT)

Water
Boil on hot embers
It needs to be bitter – no point otherwise.

WATER: THE MOTHER

She is awoken by the shooting, but she doesn't catch on immediately. At first she thinks it's a headache that wakes her because she spent too much time in the sun the previous day or perhaps, more likely, it was the fault of those two cocktails she had in order to tolerate another day at the pool with the kids. She'd give anything for an ice-cold glass of water. Johnny was spending yet another day covering the events. Some holiday, this. And to add insult to injury, he wouldn't let her take the kids and go to a pension in Kyrenia. "Best we all stick together in Nicosia." Some holiday. The pain hammers her head relentlessly. Boom boom boom boom boom. But it's footsteps she hears outside the door now, and knocking. "Madam, get dressed and take the children, go to the basement, there is a war." Where is Johnny? Johnny. She would give anything for a big glass of ice-cold water. She needs to grab the children, they need to put on their shoes – quick, to the basement. She grabs a blanket, the kids, her glasses – she doesn't think to take water. In the basement of the hotel are women, children crying, people screaming, and her children won't let go of her skirt. They sit among other women and children and they wait. Above them they hear bullets raging, they hear whistles and voices – some holiday, this, truly. She feels thirsty. She would give anything for a big glass of ice-cold water. Johnny told her that the hotel was built on a dried-up river called Pedieos. What kind of place is a place that has nothing but dry rivers? Water! She hugs the children and tells them stories about rivers and waters and waterfalls. Stories from her homeland, which is far away from here. Her children won't let go of her skirt. She reassures the other women that they are safe; she tells them that everything will be OK and that they are in no danger since they are safe in the basement. They are foreigners, they won't let anyone harm them. Above their heads the hotel is caught up in a bullet storm. A headache is hammering her head. Boom boom boom boom boom. Makarios doesn't want to let it fall into the hands of the Turks. Under no circumstances must the Big Hotel fall into Turkish hands. They constantly hear screams, explosions, trampling. She would give anything for a big glass of ice-cold water. "Madam, get dressed and get the children, go to the basement, there's a war." There's a hammering pain in her head. They will later find out that the hotel was struck by two massive mortar shells. She doesn't sleep a wink that night; she counts the hours by the pounding in her head. She would give anything for a big, huge glass of ice-cold water. Even while they're asleep, the children won't let go of her skirt. At the break of dawn, the doors open. A maid descends to the basement with a limp; she smells of lavender. Behind her follow the UN soldiers; they will lead them all to the UN vehicles. They are escorted by a UN convoy under Canadian command. On the lorry bed, the UN soldiers offer everyone a drink of water from their flasks – warm water, almost salty. Johnny had told her that the hotel was built on a dried-up river. She would give anything for a big glass of ice-cold water right now. They are all transported to the airport, and the children won't let go of her skirt, and she flies back home. Johnny will reach them later, after he has covered everything about the war. In September. From then, she will carry this thirst with her every summer and, come July, she will always feel thirsty. She will give everything for a big glass of ice-cold water.

WATER

In a big glass, ice-cold
Sometimes you have to give everything for a big glass of water.

ELDERFLOWER: THE FIANCÉE

Elderflower is mostly used for eye compresses. When your eyes hurt, you boil its flowers in water, you let it cool down a little in an earthen mug, and you wash your eyes clean with it. It's also good for drinking when you have a sore throat or a cold, but you mostly use it to wash your eyes. It's good for when you have some kind of infection or when you've cried a lot the night before and your eyes are all red or when you applied very dark grey eyeshadow to make them look pretty. At the pharmacy where she buys her vitamins they have an appreciation for medicinal herbs – the pharmacist recommends elderflower for red eyes, but she prefers to buy eye washes and drops and such. Her grandma used to make elderflower compresses back in the village. She prefers modern pharmaceuticals, modern dresses, modern times. She doesn't apply elderflower to her eyes and she doesn't want traditional things. She doesn't want a traditional wedding. She visits the Big Hotel with her Savvas to organise her wedding. She wants an orchestra and modern dances and a three-tiered wedding cake and cocktails by the pool. She goes to the hotel with her fiancé, who is a well-respected man with a good job in the public sector, and whose father had fought in the Struggle and knows the maître d' personally. Savvas doesn't want her worrying about anything. He pays for her tennis lessons at the hotel's new court with the new Italian instructor; he pays for their Saturday evening outings at the hotel, for them to dance while sipping cocktails; he pays for her expensive wedding gown with the low neckline, for her shoes with the little strap on the side, for the three-tiered cake. Her Savvas. He is well respected – his father had fought in the Struggle and he himself has an important position in his field. She doesn't want to give it too much thought, but he may one day be promoted to director, even to minister. When he speaks, she listens to him almost ecstatically: Savvas knows everything and he is an exceptional politician. His love for Greece is unsurpassed and it brings her joy to hear him speak about the government, about the need for their side to be militant and to put their foot down against foreign expansionism. In general, hearing him and being close to him brings her joy. She agrees with all his ideas – her father also took part in the Struggle and she understands how important it is. Their wedding at the Big Hotel is a major social event. When they meet with the maître d' to make all the necessary arrangements for their big day, she examines the Venetian hall with an inquisitive look, she calculates the people who are to be invited, and she wonders whether to have white roses or calla lilies on the dinner table. She definitely wants white linen table-cloths. She wants to discuss the menu with the chef and she scowls when she hears Savvas tell the maître d' that there is unrest among the Turks again. She hopes that all will go well on her wedding day and that there won't be any *troubles* like there has been in previous years. When they drive through the city in their car, Savvas knows how to avoid the checkpoints, and he changes the radio station, and they listen to music, and they discuss their honeymoon. When they set their wedding date for 27 July, she thinks about how she would like to come to this hotel on that day every year to celebrate her anniversary. When the coup breaks out, the wedding is postponed ipso facto until further notice, until they find out exactly what will happen with the situation. When, five days later, the war breaks out, Savvas, who is a reserve soldier, is drafted and deployed to serve at Pente Mili, and he is captured by the Turks and he becomes a war hostage. She waits for him for days and weeks and months, and she keeps going to the UN, not knowing if he is dead or alive. She cries incessantly and her eyes are constantly red and the only thing that soothes them are the compresses: she boils elderflower blossoms in hot water, she lets it all cool down a little in an earthen mug, and she washes her eyes with it. She listens to the news on the radio now, and she reads the newspapers to find out what's happening. She waits and waits and she washes her eyes all the time and she feels that elderflower helps her see things better, more clearly. When her husband, who was a prisoner at Adana, returns with the buses to the Big Hotel's courtyard during the hostage exchange, she is wearing flat shoes and a blouse that's buttoned up almost to her jaw despite the fact that it's September and the sun burns and is awful. She waits for hours and hours under the sun, hoping he might return. She finds it hard to believe when she sees him, when she feels him inside her arms, and she becomes aware that the other women next to her are leaving with nothing but the photos of their loved ones in their hands, and she curses those responsible, like her grandma did back in the village. She is always washing her eyes, which are always red, with elderflower: she boils elderflower in hot water, she lets it cool down a little in an earthen mug, and she washes her eyes with it. Her grandmother sends her elderflower from the village. The wedding is held three months later, with no calla lilies, no linen tablecloths, no three-tiered cakes: only tears, plenty of tears that make your eyes red.

ELDERFLOWER

In an earthen mug
You boil its flowers in hot water, you let it cool down a little,
and you wash your eyes clean with it
It's also good for drinking when you have a sore throat or a
cold, but mostly for washing your eyes
It's good for when you have an infection, or if you cried a lot
the previous night and they're all red.

SPEARMINT: THE MAYOR

Fresh spearmint with lots of sugar and warm water soothes your intestines. Dried and grated, it makes your meatballs nice and fluffy. Freshly cut from the flower bed in the morning and crushed between your fingers, it fills you with courage. It makes you smell good even when you have ugly things to talk about: politics and shit. The Mayor wants to smell nice when he is talking with the other so-called mayor about the capital's sewage system, when he goes to talk with the Turk from the other side about what to do with all the sewage and all the problems it causes in the city. Their city. The city's sewage system was supposed to be completed by the end of 1974, sometime around December, and the pipes are almost ready and the factory is under construction on the city's outskirts, in the village of Mia Milia, just outside Nicosia, and the project is coming along nicely, but then the war breaks out, the country falls apart, and there are refugees and dead people and missing people – the village of Mia Milia is now on the "Turkish side" – who has the mind to think about the sewage system any more? Three years after the invasion and the war, people hate each other to death, and everything is still fresh in their memory, but the Mayor – who has been appointed by the Archbishop, according to some, because he once said that the land belongs to its people, which enraged those in charge, and he was therefore demoted from Member of Parliament to Mayor, but who knows – thinks about the sewage as a Mayor does, thinks about the system, thinks about his city, thinks about how they can get the sewerage to function. Their city. Cunningly, he manages to insinuate himself into a dinner at which Clerides and Denktash are present, and, at some point between the wine and the zivania, he gets permission to meet with the "other" so-called mayor, from across the border, so they can talk about the sewage and the factory, that was meant to commence its operations in '74, but then war breaks out. The so-called mayor is young, he is an architect, he looks to the future, he thinks about the system. He thinks that, surely, sooner or later, a solution will be achieved. Their city will be united. The bona fide Mayor and the so-called mayor meet one day at the former's home, and they drink spearmint tea with lots of sugar, and they agree to put things down: OK, the city may be divided, but at least its sewerage can be united. "Its shit." It's a start. The Mayor receives instructions from his people: "Do what you have to do, but do not recognise the monstrosity on the other side." The so-called mayor is crucified by his people's press: "He wants to bring Greek shit over here," they say. But the regular and the so-called don't lose faith. They decide on the plan, they secure funding from a UN organisation, they find a way to address each other – they won't say "regular" and "so-called"; they'll say "each side's representative" – and they find a place to meet, too: the Big Hotel, which is located right in the middle of the capital, on the main roadblock, in a room specially configured to allow the two delegations to meet. Where else could they meet? Right in the middle. In the middle. Of their city. In the Big Hotel, the delegations meet regularly, and they decide that keeping minutes is complicated, as is talking politics – they are but two groups of the capital that want the best for their city. Every morning, before the meeting, the Mayor cuts some fresh spearmint from his flower bed, crushes it between his fingers, musters up all his courage. Sometimes he takes a few twigs to the so-called mayor too. Before the meeting, the two of them sit alone on the hotel porch: they talk about the hard stuff, about what they'll have to deal with in the meeting – they smell the spearmint in their hands. Their city. During the meetings, they drink spearmint tea with lots of sugar. They work behind the scenes and they avoid the journalists on either side. They know many wish for them to fail. Three years later, the project is completed, the system is united, and the two men decide to put it secretly into operation. First, they integrate the Russian embassy and the US embassy into the system, then they connect the hospital in the Republic's Nicosia and the Saray Hotel in the occupied side. They believe that if they announce the success of the project only after it starts running, people will be more receptive, more accepting of the news. The system is united. Subterraneously, the divided city is united. In the underground. Where the sewage flows. OK, the city is divided, but at least its sewage can be united. "Its shit." The sewage system is such a success that they decide to take things further. They design a development master plan for Nicosia, so the city's growth can take place in tandem despite the Green Line that divides it. They write things down, they meet at the Big Hotel again, they crush spearmint between their fingers, they drink litres and litres of tea with lots of sugar, they secure funding from the UN again, they find ways to pay the contractors, ways for the money to be sent to banks that aren't officially recognised. They start with two neighbourhoods torn apart by the war, Chrysaliniotissa and Arab Ahmet. Uninhabited, deserted neighbourhoods with nothing but crumbling buildings and disaster. And bullet wounds. Places where people lived who are now dead. They restore mosques and churches and old houses, they turn the old commercial streets into pedestrian areas, they try to bring young families back to the city. They manage to have the barrels and atrocious roadblocks removed across the city, and to have the soldiers removed, too, the ones who looked out at rival outposts separated only by five metres. When they run out of money, they go to Venice looking for funds with which to restore the city's Venetian walls. Their city. They go as far as Berlin, they walk around its own wall, they look at the buildings around the borders. They see the uneven development, they see the ruins. They contemplate that this isn't the picture they want to see when they unite their city. Because they will, they'll unite it – no buts, no ifs. They go on, they enable common urban development, and they create common policy systems that dictate it. They keep at it even when other projects fail, even when politics fail to resolve the big problem, even when the negotiations for a solution collapse, fail again and again. They keep at it. The master plan they leave behind continues. Even when the two of them leave their posts and become common citizens of the city. Their city. When they are awarded the big prize for development, the city is still divided. When they receive the Aga Khan Award for Architecture, the World Habitat Award, and the Europa Nostra Award for their contributions to the city during a "time of political instability", and for their efforts towards the conservation of the historical and cultural character of the walled city of Nicosia, no solution for the Cyprus problem has been achieved. When, three years into the new millennium, the roadblocks are first lifted and thousands of people gather around the checkpoint in front of the Big Hotel to cross to the "other side", they will arrange a secret meeting at the Big Hotel: they will sit on their porch for hours, crushing the spearmint that the former Mayor brings to the former Mayor and they will look at the walls of their divided city in silence and they will muster up the courage. Because it can't be. The city will be united one day. Won't their city be united one day?

SPEARMINT

Fresh, with lots of sugar and warm water, it soothes the intestines
Dried and grated, it makes meatballs fluffy
Freshly cut from the flower bed in the morning and crushed between your fingers, it fills you with courage
It makes you smell good and gives you the courage to unite your city.

HOLY WATER:
THE CLEANING LADY

In the morning, when she wakes up, she looks to the East and she prays, and she puts on her uniform, and she splashes some holy water over her face. Then she also puts some in her mouth, for the day to go well – the times are tough, and she needs her saint's assistance. Aziz Andrea is always by her side: her mum says that he saved her when she was a baby. Three days of fever and she almost died – three years old, she was – and three gallons of holy water, that's how much her mum brought from the monastery; she knelt on the floor and she pleaded with the saint, "Save her, Apostle," and she bathed her in Aziz Andrea's holy water morning and evening to send the fever away, and only Aziz Andrea's holy water made her well, only he saved her, and now the Apostle and the Prophet Muhammad always protect her. You take the holy water from its source, from the saint himself, you fill your palms with it and you splash it over your face, over your hair, you wash your eyes and you drink the holy sacred water, the saintly water from your cupped hands, you drink abundantly. You carry holy water in all the difficulties you encounter, in your glass bottle: for example, when you start working at the new hotel where cleaning ladies are needed urgently – so urgently needed that the maître d' doesn't even care whether you're Christian or not. "As long as you're clean." And silent. She works in the kitchen most of the time, peeling potatoes and washing dishes, and the salary is good and she doesn't have to talk to anyone. There are others like her, but only for scrubbing floors and cleaning dirt. The important positions in the hotel are reserved for those who speak Greek. She likes it here. Sometimes she is scared, sometimes she is bored – good thing she always carries her Aziz water with her. When she sees the young maid looking at the hotel windows and crying, she shows her how to put holy water in her hair, to send the sorrows and the pain away. One day, she offers the doorman a few drops to add to his tea that is made from rosebuds. She sprinkles it over the baby swallows that fall from their nests. Aziz wants everyone to drink his water: he is generous, he is kind. When the troubles begin, and she is forced to give up her job and leave, she leaves a gallon of holy water for the maître d' to add to his coffee and to sprinkle the building with, and she promises to come back. When she gets married, she washes her bridal dress with Aziz water and she washes her daughter's first clothes with it too. Her daughter is smart and pretty, and she grows up listening to stories about the young maid who cried while looking at the windows, about the gruelling work in the kitchen, about the old doorman with the tiny little rosebuds, and she is smart, the daughter, and she goes to university and she studies and becomes a scientist and then an architect, but still she goes regularly to get Aziz water with her mum, the former cleaning lady, because she can't say no to her mum when it comes to Aziz water. "You need to take the holy water from its source, from the saint himself, you scoop it up with your cupped hands, you splash it over your face and your hair, you wash your eyes with it and you drink abundantly, the saint wants everyone to take his water, his holy water, his Aziz water, he is generous, the Apostle, he is kind," the old cleaning lady tells her. They go together and they take the holy water, even when times are hard, when the monastery is in ruins, when the Aziz water is reserved only for the saint himself. Times like this. When people are needed to staff the bi-communal Technical Committee on Cultural Heritage – the team assigned to restore the monuments of the Muslims and the Christians – the cleaning lady's daughter, the architect, applies for the position. Muslims and Christians, Turks and Greeks participate on equal terms in the committee. The monastery of the saint of the Big Hotel's old cleaning lady is one of the first monuments to be restored, one of the first to be rescued from ruin. Other buildings will follow – other monasteries and churches and mosques and madrasas – but nothing compares to the Apostle, whose monastery they fixed, whom they saved from ruin, whose water they made flow clear again. When the committee organises the big exhibition at the Big Hotel with the works of Greek Cypriot painters that have been rediscovered in the Municipal Gallery of Famagusta forty-five years later, and the architect takes her mother, the old cleaning lady, with her to see the exhibition and her hotel – the place where she worked as a young woman – she doesn't know that her mother is secretly carrying holy water with her. The old cleaning lady roams around the once-familiar places, she looks at the works exhibited, she looks at two of them with special interest, one with the tools of the land and one with the women of her land picking cotton, and she wanders around the rooms secretly, she sneaks into her kitchen, she goes around the gardens with her daughter, she looks at the building, she looks at the ruins. The building needs fixing, it needs help, and she secretly pours some holy water over the soil from her bottle, sprinkles its walls. Aziz water helps all those who need it. You must carry holy water with you in all difficult times, in your glass bottle that you tilt towards the ground to water the soil of the hotel where you worked as a young woman that's in need of fixing, in need of help, now. You sprinkle the water wherever it is needed: the saint is generous, he offers his Aziz water to all those in need – people birds creatures soils walls buildings – he offers holy water, Aziz water.

HOLY WATER

In your glass bottle
You take it from the source, from the saint himself
You scoop it with your cupped fingers and splash your face,
you sprinkle some over your hair too
You drink abundantly from your cupped hands, you drink the
holy, the saintly water.

ROSE WATER: THE DAUGHTER

Her mother puts rose water everywhere: in food and in drinks and on her face. Best not to go out at all if you aren't going to splash some rose water on your face first: it cools you down, it tones you, it sweetens you inside. That's what they do in the hot land she's from. Her heat. Her mother puts it everywhere, rose water, not just in desserts: she adds it to the food she cooks, she sprinkles it over her head, her face, her eyes, her bosom. "I want you to sprinkle rose water on my grave," she tells her. "Sprinkle it on the cross, pour it over the soil too. To cool me down." Their heat. Every Saturday, after she's done with her chores, she takes her by the hand and they go together to Grandfather's grave and Grandmother's grave. They go the cemetery to wash the gravestones, to fill their oil lamps, to light the wicks, to sprinkle water over the soil, to water the flowers on their graves. "The dead are thirsty," her mother tells her. Their land is hot. Her mother puts it everywhere, rose water: she sprinkles it over the graves, pours it abundantly over grandfather's gravestone, and then starts chatting with the dead, she tells them her news, her pains, "the dead are thirsty," she says to her daughter, their heat, "when I die, I want you to bury me right here," she says, "I want you to sprinkle my soil, to sprinkle my grave with rose water – here, together with Grandma and Grandpa." That's what they do on Saturdays, and then they go away happy for having poured rose water over the dead, for having quenched their thirst. She promises, she looks at the sun, she looks at the heat, she lifts her face up. Every Saturday, she says – she promises. Their heat. The dead are thirsty. They want you to chat with them, they want to hear your news. Her mum manages to make it to the other side before the war, a few months before the summer. She dies, and they leave the village and take nothing with them – not their clothes, not their books, not the house keys – they take nothing, not even the rose water. They just close the door in a hurry, don't even lock it. And of all the things that pained her when they lost everything, when they had to flee, of all those things, the thing that pained her most was that her mother's grave was left unwatered. It remains unwatered and unsprinkled and dry for thirty or so years, her mother's grave. When the checkpoints open and everyone queues up right next to the Big Hotel for hours and hours so they can cross to the others, so they can go across to see their homes, to see their land, she takes a gallon of rose water with her to sprinkle over her mother's grave, to wash the tombstones at the cemetery, to pour abundantly over Grandma's grave and Grandpa's grave. She wants to tell her mother her news, to water her grave with rose water. The dead are thirsty. Their heat. But she waits at the crossing for hours, she waits and waits and nothing happens, she waits under the sun for endless hours with thousands of others, and she waits in the heat, she waits in their heat, and in the end she pours the rose water over herself, over her face, and over the others, pours it over them, over their heads and over their faces – they all ran out of water a while ago. Her heat. Their heat. She sprinkles it over everyone, the rose water. Best not to leave the house at all if you're not going to sprinkle your face with rose water first: it cools you down, it tones you, it sweetens you inside. Seven hours she waits, seven hours she stands on her feet at the crossing so she can cross over. She waits by the Big Hotel so she can pour some rose water over her mother's grave, so she can tell her mum her news, her thirty years' worth of pains, waits with all those who wait, with all those who want to go and visit their homes and their land, and then she runs out of rose water and she runs out of tears: her face dries up, everything dries up under the sun and the heat, their heat – the sun dries everything up.

ROSE WATER

*You can put it in drinks, in the food you cook, in your bosom
and on your face
Best not to leave the house at all if you aren't going to sprinkle
your face with rose water first, to cool you down, to tone you,
to sweeten you inside.*

KITROMILAKI LIQUEUR:
THE SINGER

Grandma never did like George Dalaras. "Sprout of Turkish seed – bad luck," she tells her. "What are you talking about, Grandma?" Quiet! Grandma knows. He's the one who brought the Turks. Him. That son of a gun. Grandma knows because, number one, he never smiles – she's seen him in all the magazines – and, number two, she has talked to him. They've met. When? In the 70s, early 70s, right around that time. Grandma was young then, and beautiful, and she had her hair plaited in two thick black braids that looked like snakes in the spring – that thick, her braids were, if you can imagine it. In her village, where Turks and Greeks live together, there was a Hasan who called her "Dünya güzeli". The world's prettiest. That's how pretty she was, if you can imagine it. And she was modest, too, and hard-working. Every second Thursday of the month, in the afternoon, Grandma went to the Big Hotel and she sold the baby bitter orange liqueur that she made with her mother and put in nice white bottles. They had a citrus orchard at home. They also made mandarin liqueur, orange liqueur, and another liqueur, which is a little bitter, made from kumquats. But no liqueur compared to Seville orange liqueur. And not many people could make it, not many people knew how to make it. You needed to soak its peels in zivania for seven days, times three – twenty-one days – and then you needed to add lots of sugar. How much sugar and how many orange peels is a bit of a secret. Not many people made it, not many people knew how to make kitromilaki liqueur. It's a beverage made from this tasteless fruit, the tart baby bitter orange, this fruit that you can't eat as it is, that you can only make spoon sweets out of or squeeze into soups and add to your food. That's the kind of fruit it is, if you can imagine it. It's a drink that's mostly good for making cakes, but which you can also drink in a slim little glass on happy days, at celebrations, at Christmas. And it makes you smile. And it's in high demand at the Big Hotel too, and it's nice to go there every other Thursday, it's nice to sell it there at the Big Hotel so they can use it in the cakes they make, enormous white sponge cakes, or as a base for a cocktail. Every second Thursday, Grandma, who at the time was young and very pretty, put on her good apron, braided her hair tightly – her black hair, her thick black hair that looked like snakes in the spring – and put the liqueur in her basket, in her nice white bottles, and she took the bus from Famagusta. She got off at the capital and she sold her bottles. She goes into the Big Hotel's kitchen with her basket and she sells her liqueur and she sits for a while, chatting with the kitchen staff, who offer her coffee. Sometimes the chef also offers her a piece of leftover cake, that white sponge cake drizzled in her Seville orange liqueur, and sometimes she chats with the old doorman, who offers her dry rosebuds in his glass jar. Sometimes she exchanges recipes with the maids and the cleaning ladies. She likes it here. One day – may that day be cursed – it must have been September or October, she doesn't know how, but she gets lost, gets mixed up, mistakes one door for another, one wall for another, and instead of going to the kitchen ends up in that pond in the hotel where she sees those naked women in their swimsuits and their hair all loose and washed out and they are rehearsing for some competition. So they can choose the prettiest. And next to them Dalaras, singing. Her grandma looks at them, and seeing them in their knickers and their high heels in broad daylight in front of everyone makes her sick to her stomach. And what do they do? They look at her and start giggling, they laugh at her, at her good apron, at her hair, which is black like snakes in the spring, and Grandma loses her footing and she trips, and all her liqueur, her kitromilaki liqueur, falls at her feet, and there goes the liqueur, there goes her good apron too. Dalaras, who sees her, laughs sarcastically. The waiters come to clean everything up and there's a general sense of commotion and Grandma feels ashamed, humiliated. Her knees fail her. She leaves, and it's weeks and months before she goes back to sell her baby bitter orange liqueur again. Three years later, on 15 July, at exactly 8.20 in the morning, she turns on the radio and she hears George Dalaras singing "The Sea-Blue Shirt," and at that moment, immediately, Makarios dies, and the people in the tanks come, may they all be cursed once and twice and three times, and the coup happens and then the Turks come and the sirens start wailing. Not in this exact order, perhaps: it's been fifty years or so, she can't possibly remember everything. But what she does know is that it was all the fault of Dalaras, who sang nonchalantly on the radio while the world around her crumbled. And who laughed at her and broke her bottles too. Her baby bitter orange liqueur. Grandma knows all too well. She sees him in all the magazines: his face that never smiles, his conceited face. And nobody likes him, either. The only time he laughed was at her. And when, later on, he starts doing those big concerts to raise money – so he says – for the defence of Cyprus, when he sings so he can take people's money and then give it back to us so we can buy weapons and tanks to safeguard the Hellenism of Cyprus and whatnot, Grandma observes him suspiciously and she says that something about this whole situation stinks. "How do you know all this, Grandma?" Grandma knows. And she won't let her go to the concerts either, the ones for our national defence and whatnot so that they can buy weapons with her money – she won't even let her sing those songs about Cyprus she puts on the record player. "What does he know about us? What does he know about waiting? Does Dalaras *wait night and day*?" she says pointedly, and Grandma remembers Hasan

89

and "Dünya güzeli." A few years later, when that concert takes place, the one with that handsome Greek guy, whatshisname, and the other guy, the Turk, Sakis and Burak? the concert next to the Big Hotel, the one organised by the UN, the one that makes our people here and the people there too upset and they don't want them singing there, Grandma wants to go to the concert. She is all fired up and she manages to convince her, and they go to the Big Hotel and they pass through security gasping for air – with their souls in their mouths, as they say – and they walk past the people demonstrating and screaming, and they go to the concert and they have a good time and she takes two bottles too, Grandma does, two beautiful white bottles of kitromilaki liqueur, to give as presents to Sakis and Burak. She gives the bottles to the UN people so they can pass them on to the boys, delicious kitromilaki liqueur to pour in a tall slim glass and to put in cakes too, if they want. The drink that makes you smile. Because they came to sing for peace, she tells her, Sakis and Burak came here, next to the Big Hotel, the one where she used to sell her liqueur in her youth, her kitromilaki liqueur – and also because nobody wants them, not our people, not their people either. Moments like this call for kitromilaki liqueur, which is a drink that makes you smile. Vastly superior, she says of Sakis, much better than that sulky jinx Dalaras, and more handsome too.

KITROMILAKI LIQUEUR

In a slim little glass
For joys, peace concerts, Christmas
Makes you smile.

GRAPE MOLASSES: THE BUILDER

He's had mouth sores for as long as he can remember. He's very sensitive. His doctor says it's the stress. As soon as something stresses him out, as soon as he feels anxious, his gums start bleeding, his mouth fills up with tiny little holes so painful they crush him. He can't eat; he can't drink either, and there's no drug he hasn't tried – nothing helps. The only thing that seems to make a difference is the grape molasses an old lady whose house he fixes gives him. Grape juice molasses that you boil for hours and hours, that you boil and boil until the liquid turns thick like honey – you dab it on your lips and on your gums and it's the only thing that can cure mouth ulcers, those little holes in your mouth. Grape molasses. And it tastes good too, at least. The thing that stresses him out is when he can't get a job done – when, for example, they call on him to restore one of those old houses, the "cultural heritage" houses, and he can't bring the job to a close. When the house's foundations are all worn down, when the walls are full of humidity, when the adobe – the

bricks villagers made in the old times from straw and mud –
starts to crumble and fall to the floor, when the oak rafters
can no longer support the roof. Whenever a house is on the
verge of falling apart, they call him, they call Hasan the anxious to come fix it. The builder. Only a handful of people
know old architecture like he does, only a handful of people
have mastered the old art with which people used to build
their homes, only a handful of them know how to repair the
ancient materials used in the foundations – and even fewer
people know how to *feel* old houses, how to understand
them. When they call on him to have a look at one of these
houses, he knows things are going to be tough. He asks to be
left alone with the house so he can see, so he can assess, so
he can figure out what is salvageable. He visits the house in
the morning when the light is still clear; he places his hand
on the walls, he feels the humidity, he digs the ground with
his nail, he climbs up the roof to see how well the wood and
the reeds are holding up, he smells the mildew, he digs until
he finds the old yellow sandstone holding up the verandas
at the entrance. He leans with his back against the old walls,
he lies face down on the floor, he looks at the corners, the
broken floor tiles, the nooks in the walls; he lets the house
talk to him. He closes his eyes and listens to the whispers
and the sighs of those who once lived there and to what
will come. That's usually when his mouth fills with ulcers,
when the stress takes over him. It's when the house starts
talking to him, when the house itself tells him what needs
to be done, whether it wants to be repaired and filled with

people and to come alive again or whether it wants to die. Sometimes the house itself tells him it doesn't need fixing. Sometimes it wants its adobe, with its mud and its straw, to return to the earth, for its stones to become one with the ground. Ashes to ashes, or whatever they say – that. When a house is about to collapse, when it's about to go to smithereens, he's the one they always call to the rescue: anxious Hasan of the walls, the builder. They call on him to come and fix it. That's why his mouth is always full of sores. When, in strict confidence, he is asked to go to the Big Hotel, to see and assess and say what needs to be done to salvage it, he knows for a fact that his mouth is about to get bloody. The person who approaches him tells him that they'd like him to carry out an evaluation "of these old walls that have once known great glories". The man doesn't reveal much, but Hasan manages to find out that the Church, which owns the hotel, intends to sell it to an American investor who wants to do it up, have it renovated, turn it into the pride of Nicosia that it once was. As far as they understand, he says, the building is in terrible shape inside and out, and even the UN people who once used the rooms on the top floors as accommodation are now staying in containers. "It's hazardous," says the man, "and has consequently been abandoned. We want you to see if you can salvage it." The anxious builder goes there one morning when the light is still bright to figure out whether the hotel can be salvaged. The job is urgent, the investor needs answers fast. When he approaches the building, he first faces the entrance, the yellow sandstone facade pierced by bullets, tiny holes that can crush you with pain. He enters the building, he walks to the big Venetian hall, he runs his hand across the walls, feels the humidity, digs at the marble with his nails, smells the mildew in the air, leans with his back against the old walls, then lies face down on the floor, then looks at the corners in the big lounge, at the cracked floor tiles at the entrance, at the nooks in the walls, and he hears the squeaking of the rats, and he feels his mouth fill with sores. He closes his eyes and he hears the whispers and the sighs of those who once lived there and what's to come. The building talks to him but, for the first time, anxious Hasan of the walls can't make out what it wants. Does it want for its marbles to return to the ground? For its stones to become one with the soil? Ashes to ashes or whatever it's called? That thing there? Does it want to be repaired, to be filled with people again, to come alive again, or does it want to die? Hasan the anxious doesn't know; the builder cannot understand what this big house is telling him and this stresses him out. It stresses him out very much. What he feels is pain. He tries again, he goes again and again; he touches the walls, he rolls on the floor, he climbs the windows. The building does not respond. At night, he returns home and can't sleep: his mouth hurts, his gums hurt, the dozens of tiny holes in his mouth that look like bullet wounds hurt. When the man who approached him calls him again, he doesn't know what his verdict is going to be. When current affairs beat him to it, and the American investor retracts his interest in the hotel and, with it, his investments, he can't get the building out of his head. Never before has a building refused to speak to him, never has a building not trusted him with its future. What he feels is pain. One day, he goes to the grocer and buys dozens of bottles of grape molasses for his lips, which are by now bleeding almost constantly. Then one morning he walks past the checkpoint and he sneaks into the hotel and he pours gallons of molasses over the walls. When the UN arrest him and hand him over to his people, he whispers that the only thing that can help heal holes is grape molasses. Only it can take the pain away. They grab him, remove him from the premises, but as they do he manages to look back: he sees the molasses trickling down the building and, for the first time, notices that the molasses is a dark red colour that looks just right on the hotel's walls, looks just right for the hotel's blood, fills the bullet wounds with red. Until the rain washes them clean again.

GRAPE MOLASSES

Molasses from grape juice, which you boil until it becomes thick like honey
You put it on your lips, you put it on your gums
Only it can heal your sores, the tiny holes in your mouth, your walls that have been pierced by bullets.

LEMONADE: THE UN

In truth, only lemonade can help you bear the heat. Especially if you make it yourself. They make a nice lemonade with brown sugar and sour lemons on the island. One part brown sugar and one part lemon juice. The island has good lemons. There are times in the afternoon when that's the only thing that can quench her thirst. Lemonade with brown sugar and sour lemons. She buys lemons and she squeezes them. She slowly adds the brown sugar. She's become good at it. Only lemonade can help you bear the lies and the heat. She didn't know much about the island before she got here. They've talked to them about the English, about the Greeks and the Turks, about the intercommunal clashes, about the Muslims and the Christians, about the checkpoints; you don't assume duties in a place, war zone or no war zone, unless you are fully cognisant of the situation on the ground. She is well aware of the situation now. They've told them about the war. It's like everything is always at war on the island. These things she knows. The UN have been lodging at the Big Hotel since 1974. Since the Turkish invasion and the war. The hotel has been their home ever since. They live in the rooms, they cook in the spacious kitchen, dine in its Venetian hall on Saturdays, the English drink beers at the wooden bar and the Argentinians drink maté in the jasmine garden, where someone has planted cactuses. Some people put on loud English music in the evenings and play darts against the hotel's walls. Many get drunk and remember their homeland. The UN have been lodging at the hotel since 1974. After the Turkish invasion, after the war. The hotel has been their home ever since – until recently, when it started to crumble and they were all forced to move into those atrocious containers. She is well aware of the situation – they've told them all about it all, they've been told all about it. But nobody warned them about the lies and the heat. And good God how they lie in this place and how unbelievable the heat is. So many lies they say in this Big Hotel when they gather here, when they have meetings to solve the Problem – so many lies that, when the people who talk of a solution on the island leave, she grabs a broom to sweep the floor, to sweep away all the lies they left behind. She fills rubbish bags brimful with lies and she throws them out into the bins for the cats to play with. So many lies they tell, such incredible heat there is at the Big Hotel, the kind of heat that fills your lungs with hot air, that dries the air in your nostrils, that dries up your face, that chops you up into pieces, that won't let you breathe. The kind of heat that forces everything into absolute stillness: the cicadas, the people, the trees, the cats. A hellish heat. That's the kind of heat it is. Summer noons in Nicosia are dead and languid, and all she can do is sleep in the container that has been placed in the courtyard to be used as a room. Sometimes she swims in the pool and, less often, she plays tennis with a colleague at night, when the temperature drops sufficiently to make it bearable. Beyond the pool and the tennis court and the dining hall with the ramshackle flooring, nothing in the hotel is in use any more. And nothing outside it, either – there's nothing to do on this Green Line, and there's definitely nothing green about it. All you can do is feel thirsty. And drink lemonade. Sometimes she takes a walk around the building, wanders around the rooms, looks at the crumbling plaster, trips over the ramshackle floors, hears the rats in the attic. Sometimes she goes outside and walks between the two checkpoints. Sometimes she just stands there and looks at the building from afar, sometimes she thinks that one of these days the hotel will come crashing down, will go to smithereens, will collapse, will succumb to its own rubble. They will wake up one day and find it dead among the ruins, killed by the war, the heat, the lies. One day, she thinks, they'll wake up and they'll find it dead and everyone will cry and they will all look at each other trying to figure out who is to blame. The heat and the war and the lies will kill the building. And all the lemons in the world, all the water, all the tears shed won't be enough to save it.

LEMONADE

You squeeze the lemons
Brown sugar,
equal parts lemon juice and sugar
You pour into a bottle, you stir until the sugar melts
You dilute with cold water
Only lemonade can help you bear
the lies and the heat.

TEARS: THE GRIFFIN

He has cried three times in his life. When the war was over and the Germans were defeated, when his son was finally born, and today, when he is overseeing everything just before the hotel's inauguration. He is anxious, walking back and forth to make sure everything is in its right place – the snacks and the trays full of drinks, the well-polished cutlery, the porcelain plates. He straightens a napkin here, he places a glass a little further here, he polishes a doorknob with his handkerchief, he wipes a tear away from his eye. The Italian chandelier glows even in the dark; the marble floors shine. Everything is ready and waiting for the people to come and, really, everyone who's anyone will want to be here tonight. Be they English governors or wealthy Nicosians, be they haughty priests and clerics or Turkish lawyers with expensive cars who reign supreme in the British courts of the old town. Everyone will be here shortly to participate in the inauguration of the best, the most beautiful, the most dazzling, most lavish hotel this land has ever seen. A hotel that, he knows, deep inside, will become the most precious gem of the island, of all of the Middle East, and that will welcome famous people, thousands of important foreigners. His Big Hotel, the beginning of new, better times. The flagship of a better world. This is what he believes, and let some people call him foolish and romantic, because nothing can go wrong; he truly believes it now, he has taken his measures, he has studied everything in the tiniest detail, he has made sure the entrance door is guarded by a griffin – as all palaces must be. When they were looking for the symbol that would represent the Big Hotel, he remembered the ring and the story his father used to tell him about the griffin, the ring with the seal that his father had given him when he was young. Griffins are the guardians of grand palaces. They stand guard at their entrances and they watch over them and keep them safe. They have a vulture's head and a lion's body, and they stand at the entrance of big houses and they keep evil out. They are formidable, legendary beasts, and they feed on secrets and hopes and tears. At the entrance of the Big Hotel is a huge griffin carved on the floor. He is made of Greek marble and painted blue, and he stands guard at the door and looks after the palace. He stands guard at the entrance and he won't let any lies or any evil pass through. He'll watch over the palace and make sure it stands strong. Griffins are animals of Mesopotamia and of the Middle East, but sometimes they settle in our part of the world too. They are symbols of an old world and good wishes for the future. In the old times, people used to say that griffins were fantastic guardians, that they did their job very well, that they took great care of the palaces they protected, but that, sometimes, on rare occasions, they might fail. And this makes them cry. The griffin sheds tears. Even when he's carved out of stone or marble, a griffin will cry if he can't do his job right. If he can't keep the palace safe from evil. This is what his father often says. And yet, look, the doors are opening, the people are rushing inside, the Big Hotel is starting to glow, it's starting to glow as grand and magnificent palaces that herald new beginnings do. The waiters usher in the people with their perfectly ironed clothes, not a single crease, and their trays full, and the guests start drinking, and they grab brandy sours from the trays and lavender teas and Commandaria, the ancient wine, and cognac and ayran and rosebud infusions and orgeat and beer water coffee rose water and grape molasses and lemonade, every drink under the sky is here. Take ye, and drink. This building is made to live and shine eternally. He has cried three times in his life. Once when the Germans were defeated, once when his son finally came into the world, and once today, at the inauguration ceremony, when the palace opens its doors. The Palace of Ledra. Of Nicosia. The Ledra Palace. He looks at the lights, he looks at the people, and he knows that all will finally be well. Tonight inaugurates the hotel and with it too a new beginning, a new life. He looks at the lights, he looks at the people, he looks down as well, towards the ancient guardian, and he nods to him, reminds him to take good care of the palace. And there it is: one of the waiters suddenly trips and drops some ice cubes on the floor. He makes haste to pick them up with his handkerchief – he doesn't want anyone to slip and fall. But before he does, there it is, the ice melting inside the beast's eyes, the ice turning to water, running from the beast's eyes.

TEARS

Cold
Sometimes not even griffins can protect magical palaces.

Foundry Editions
40 Randolph Street
London NW1 0SR
United Kingdom

Copyright © S. Patakis S.A. (Patakis Publishers) and Constantia Soteriou 2022

First published in 2022 as *Brandy Sour* by S. Patakis S.A. (Patakis Publishers), Athens

Translation © Lina Protopapa 2024

This first edition published by Foundry Editions in 2024

The moral right of Constantia Soteriou to be identified as the Author of this work has been asserted in accordance with the Copyright, Designs and Patents Act 1988.

A CIP record for this title is available from the British Library.

ISBN 978-1-7384463-0-8

Series cover design by Murmurs Design
Designed and typeset in LfA Aluminia by Tetragon, London
Printed and bound by TJ Books, Padstow, Cornwall

foundryeditions.co.uk

MARIA GRAZIA CALANDRONE

Your Little Matter

Translation by Antonella Lettieri

ITALY

Rome, 1965. A man and a woman, excluded from Italian society, abandon their eight-month-old daughter in the Villa Borghese and take extreme action. In 2021, that child, author Maria Grazia Calandrone, sets out to discover the truth about what happened, examining the places where her mother lived, suffered, worked, and loved.

Your Little Matter is a reconstruction of the life and death of a parent, a shocking insight into the real lives of marginalised women from the Italian South, and the examination of a cause célèbre that was a catalyst for social change in Italy. Combining poetic insight with journalistic investigation, the personal and the public, the book tells a devastating story of how the institutionalised callousness of state and society can lead to tragedy.

Your Little Matter was shortlisted for the 2023 Premio Strega.

ROSA RIBAS

Far

Translation by Charlotte Coombe

SPAIN

In a residential development in the middle of nowhere, one of the many that were begun in Spain but never finished, lives a small community of neighbours trying to lead a normal life, despite being far from anything. On the development that promised every luxury, beyond the streets that lead nowhere, behind a high metal fence, the unfinished houses menace the inhabitants and become occupied by people on the fringes of society whom the Crash has destroyed.

Rosa Ribas's two unnamed protagonists come from different sides of this fence. The atmospheric, disturbing, and addictive story of their growing relationship is half quirky love story and strong commentary on how easily people can fall through the cracks in society. Although the message is entirely universal, the context is delicious and uniquely Spanish.

**FOUNDRY
EDITIONS**